C000256269

Latin Collection
23 classic songs for keyboard

© International Music Publications Ltd
First published in 2000 by International Music Publications Ltd
International Music Publications Ltd is a Faber Music company
3 Queen Square, London WC1N 3AU

Music arranged & processed by Barnes Music Engraving Ltd
Cover Image: Getty Images

Printed in England by Caligraving Ltd
All rights reserved

ISBN10: 0-571-52833-3
EAN13: 978-0-571-52833-2

Agua De Beber

Words and Music by A C Jobim and Vinicius De Moraes

Suggested Registration: Saxophone
Rhythm: Bossa Nova
Tempo: ♩ = 120

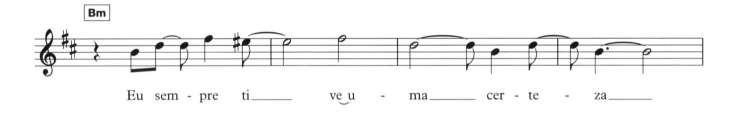

Eu sem - pre ti_____ ve u - ma_____ cer - te - za_____

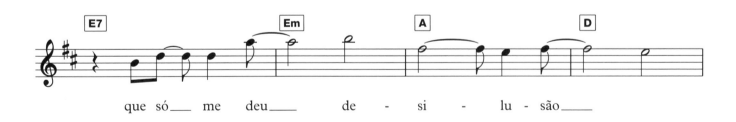

que só__ me deu__ de - si - lu - são__

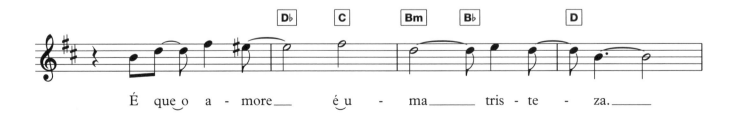

É que o a - more__ é u - ma__ tris - te - za.__

Mui - ta má - go a de - mais pa - ra um Co -

- ra - ção.___ Á - gua de Be - ber,_____

Á - gua de Be - ber,_____ ca - ma - rá.__ Á - gua de Be - ber,_____

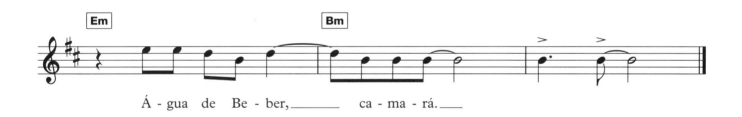

Á - gua de Be - ber,_____ ca - ma - rá.__

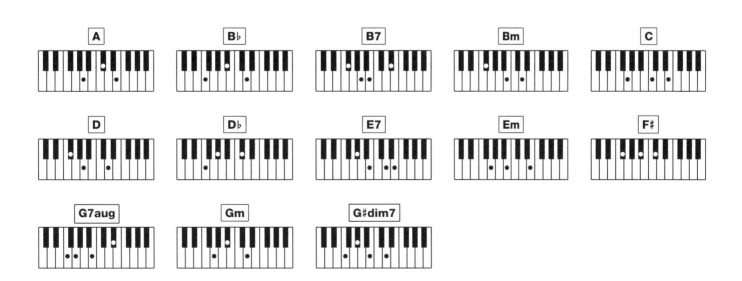

Amor Amor

English Words by Norman Newell
Spanish Words by Ricardo Lopez Mendez
Music by Gabriel Ruiz

Suggested Registration: Spanish Guitar
Rhythm: Cha-Cha
Tempo: ♩ = 120

A - mor, a - mor, a - mor.＿＿＿＿ This word so

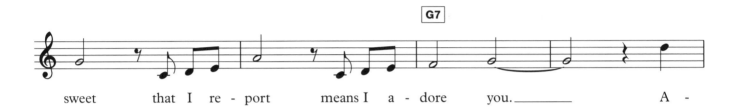

sweet that I re - port means I a - dore you.＿＿＿ A -

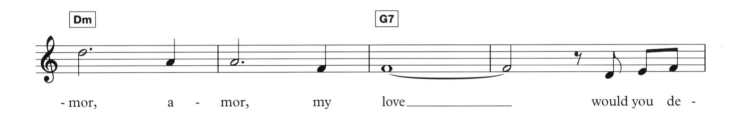

- mor, a - mor, my love＿＿＿＿＿ would you de -

- ny this heart that I have placed be - fore you. I

can't find an - oth - er word with mean - ing so clear, my lips try to whis - per sweet - er

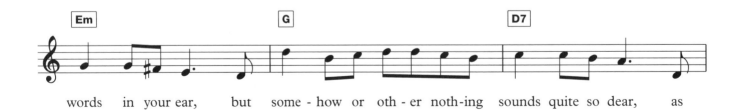

words in your ear, but some - how or oth - er noth - ing sounds quite so dear, as

this soft car - ess - ing word I know. A - mor, a -

- mor, a - mor._____ When you're a - way, there is no

day and night's are lone - ly._____ A - mor, a -

- mor, my love,_____ make life di - vine, say you'll be

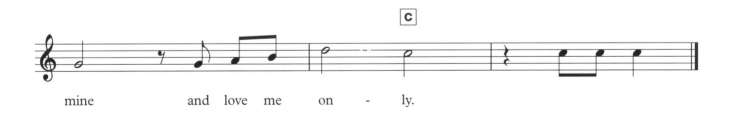

mine and love me on - ly.

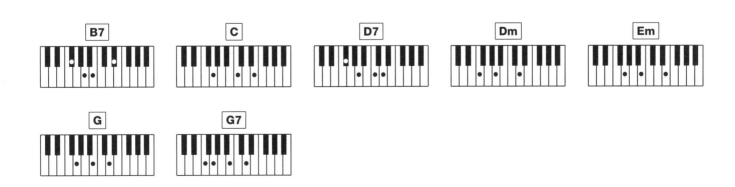

Begin The Beguine

Words and Music by Cole Porter

Suggested Registration: Piano / Strings
Rhythm: Beguine
Tempo: ♩ = 112

When they be - gin _____ the be - guine, it

brings back the sound _____ of mu - sic so ten - der,

it brings back a night _____ of trop - ic - al

splen - dour, it brings back a me -

- mo - ry ev - er - green. I'm

with you once more_____ un - der the stars,

and down by the shore_____ an or - ches-tra's

play - ing and e - ven the stars_____

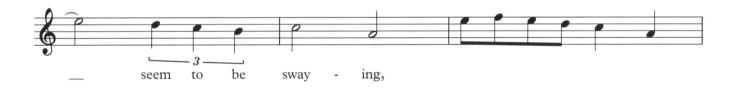

___ seem to be sway - ing,

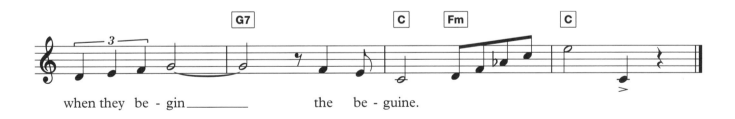

when they be - gin_____ the be - guine.

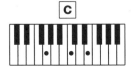
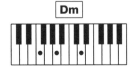
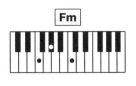

CHERRY PINK AND APPLE BLOSSOM WHITE

Music by Louiguy

Suggested Registration: Trumpet
Rhythm: Cha-Cha
Tempo: ♩ = 126

It's cher-ry pink and ap-ple blos-som white, when your true lov-er comes your

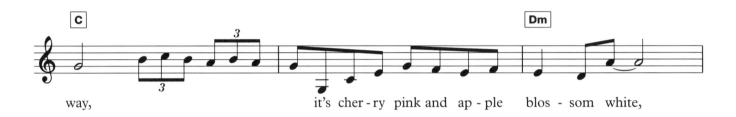

way, it's cher-ry pink and ap-ple blos-som white,

the po-ets say. The sto-ry goes that once a

cher-ry tree,— be-side an ap-ple tree did grow,

and there a boy once met his bride to be,— long, long a-

-go. The boy looked in-to her eyes,— it was a

sight to en - thrall, the bree-zes joined in their sighs, the blos-soms start-ed to fall__ and as they

gent-ly car - essed, the lov-ers looked up to find__ the branch-es of the two trees were in - ter -

- twined and that is why the po - ets al - ways write: If there's a new moon bright a -

- bove, it's cher - ry pink and ap - ple blos - som white,

when you're in love.

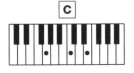

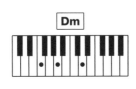

CONGA

Words and Music by Enrique E Garcia

Suggested Registration: Jazz Guitar
Rhythm: Samba
Tempo: ♩ = 120

Come __ on shake your bo-dy ba-by, do the con - ga, know

__ you can't con-trol your-self a-ny long-er, come on shake your bo-dy ba-by, do the con-ga, know

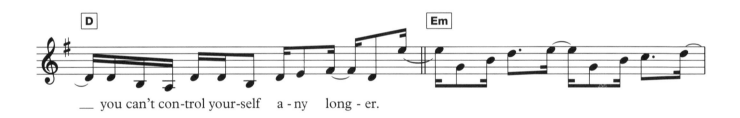

__ you can't con-trol your-self a - ny long - er.

Come_ on shake your bo-dy ba-by, do the con - ga,   know

_ you can't con-trol your-self a-ny long-er, come   on shake your bo-dy ba-by, do the con-ga,   know

_ you can't con-trol your-self a-ny   long-er.

Desafinado

Words and Music by A C Jobim and Newton Ferreira De Mendonca
English Translation by John Hendrix and Jessie Cavanaugh

Suggested Registration: Acoustic Guitar
Rhythm: Bossa Nova
Tempo: ♩ = 120

Love is like a ne-ver end-ing me-lo-dy, po-ets have com-

-pared it to a sym-pho-ny, a sym-pho-ny con-duct-ed by the

light-ing of the moon, but our song of love is slight-ly out of tune.

Once your kiss-es raised me to a fe-ver pitch,

now the orch-est-ra-tion does-n't seem so rich, seems to me you've

changed the tune we used to sing, like the bos-sa no-va love should

swing. We used to har-mon-ise, two souls in per-fect time,

DINDI

Words and Music by A C Jobim, Louis Oliveira and Ray Gilbert

Suggested Registration: Jazz Guitar
Rhythm: Bossa Nova
Tempo: ♩ = 90

Oh Din - di, if I on - ly had words I would

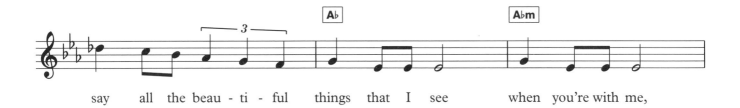

say all the beau - ti - ful things that I see when you're with me,

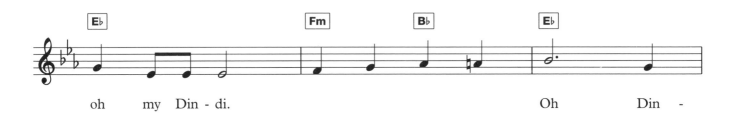

oh my Din - di. Oh Din -

- di, like the song of the wind in the trees, that's how my heart is

sing - ing Din - di, hap - py Din - di, when you're with me.

I love you more each day,_____ yes I

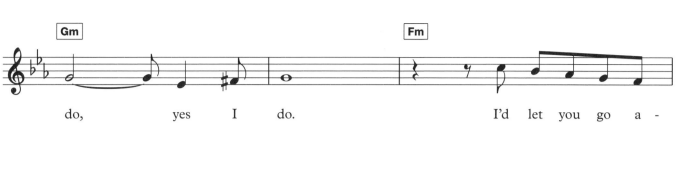

do,　yes I　do.　I'd let you go a -

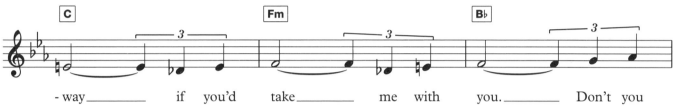

- way＿＿＿ if you'd take＿＿＿ me with you.＿＿＿ Don't you

know　Din - di,　I'd be　run - ning and search - ing　for

you,　like a ri - ver that　can't find the sea,　that would be me　with-out

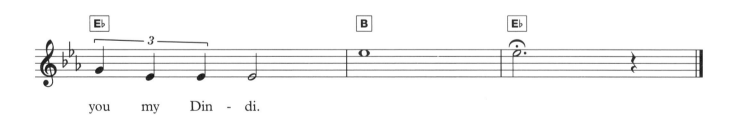

you　my　Din - di.

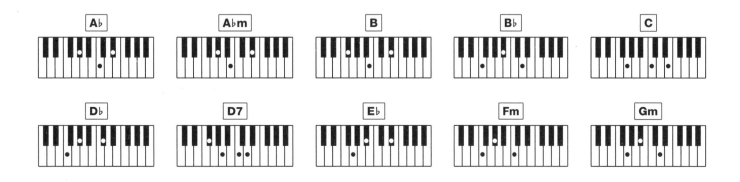

FEELINGS

Words and Music by Morris Albert and Louis Gaste

Suggested Registration: Pan Flute
Rhythm: Bossa Nova
Tempo: ♩ = 110

La Bamba

Adapted and Arranged by Ritchie Valens

Suggested Registration: Brass
Rhythm: 8 Beat
Tempo: ♩ = 150

Pa-ra bai-lar la Bam - ba,   pa-ra bai-lar la Bam-

-ba se ne-ce - si-ta una po-co de gra-cia.

Un-a po-ca de gra-cia para mi para ti y a-ri-ba ya-ri-

-ba,   ya - ri - ba ya - ri-ba por ti se-

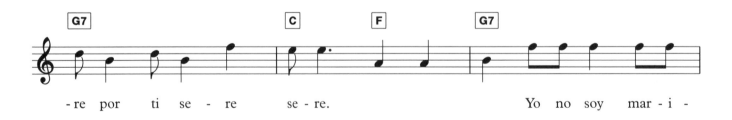

-re por ti se-re se-re.   Yo no soy mar-i-

-ne-ro,   yo no soy mar-i - ne-ro, soy cap-i-

-tan, yo no soy mar - i - ne - ro, soy cap - i - tan.

Bam - ba, Bam - ba, Bam - ba,

Bam - ba, Bam - ba, Bam - ba,

Bam - ba, Bam - ba,

Bam - ba, Bam - ba.

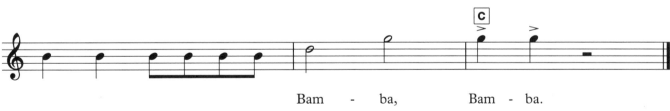

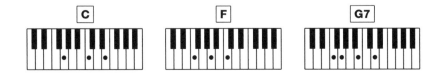

Livin' La Vida Loca

Words and Music by Robi Rosa and Desmond Child

Suggested Registration: Solo Flute
Rhythm: Mambo
Tempo: ♩ = 88

She's in - to su-per-sti - tion, black cats and voo-doo dolls,___

and I feel a pre-mo - ni - tion that girl's gon-na make me fall.___

She's in - to new sen-sa-tions, new kicks in the can-dle light, _ she's got a man ad-dic-tion

s'full ev - 'ry day and night,_ she'll make you take your clothes off and_ go_ dan-

- cing in_ the rain,_ she'll make_ you live_ her cra - zy life_ or she'll take

The Macarena

Words and Music by Antonio Romero and Rafael Ruiz

Suggested Registration: Electric Guitar
Rhythm: Samba (Salsa)
Tempo: ♩ = 104

Oa-lea tu cuer-poa-le-gri-a Ma-ca-re-na que tu Cuer-poes pa dar-lea-le-gri-ay co-sa bue-na

Oa - lea tu cuer-poa-le-gri-a Ma-ca-re-na Eh____ Ma - ca - re-na.

Oa - lea tu cuer-poa-le-gri-a Ma-ca-re-na que tu Cuer-poes pa dar - lea-le-gri-ay co-sa bue-na

Oa - lea tu cuer-poa-le-gri-a Ma-ca-re-na Eh____ Ma - ca - re-na.

When I dance they call__ me Ma-ca-re-na and the boys, they say 'que estoy bue-na',

they all want me, they can't have me, so they all come and dance be-side me,

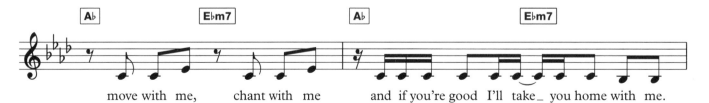

move with me, chant with me and if you're good I'll take__ you home with me.

Manha De Carnaval

Words by Antonia Maria
Music by Luiz Bonfa

Suggested Registration: Marimba
Rhythm: Rhumba
Tempo: ♩ = 100

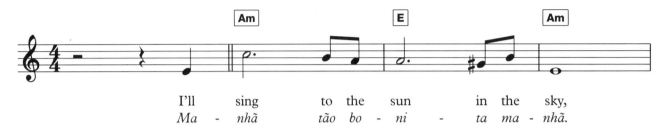

I'll sing to the sun in the sky,
Ma - nhã tão bo - ni - ta ma - nhã.

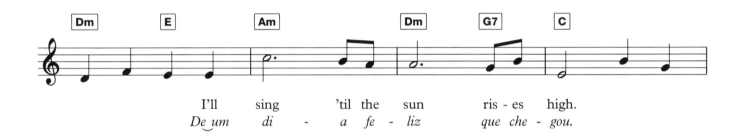

I'll sing 'til the sun ris - es high.
De um di - a fe - liz que che - gou.

Car-ni-val time is here, mag-ic-al time of year,
O sol ne céu sur-giu E em ca-da côr bril-hou

and as the time draws near dreams lift my heart.
vol tou o son - ho en-tão Ao co-ra - çao.

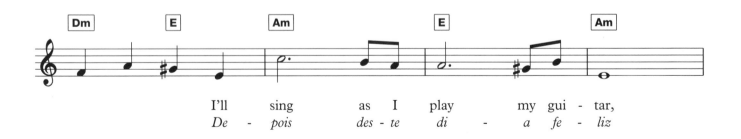

I'll sing as I play my gui - tar,
De - pois des-te di - a fe - liz

Mi Tierra

Words and Music by Gloria Estefan

Suggested Registration: Saxophone
Rhythm: Salsa
Tempo: ♩ = 100

De mi tie-rra be - lla,   de mi tie-rra san - ta,

Oi-go e se gri-to de los tam-bo - res, y los tim-ba-les al__ cum-ban-

- char.__   Y e-se pre - gón que can-ta un her-ma - no,   que de su

tie - rra vi-ve le-ja - no,   y que el re - cuer-do le ha-ce llo-rar.__   U-na can

ción que vi-ve en-to-nan-do,   de su do - lor de su pro-pie llan - to,   y__

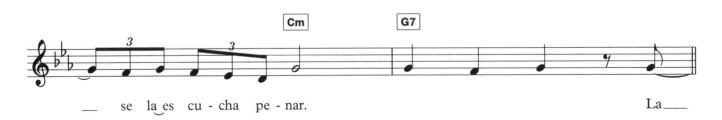

__ se la es-cu-cha pe - nar.   La__

_ tie - rra _ te due - le, la_____ tie - rra_ te - da, _ en -

- me - dio_ del al - ma,_ cuan - do tú_ no es - tás._ La_

_ tie - rra_ te em - pu - ja de - ra - iz - y cal,_ la_

_ tie - rra_ sus - pi - ra si - no te_ ve más,_ la_

_ tie - rra_ sus - pi - ra, si_ no te_ ve mas._

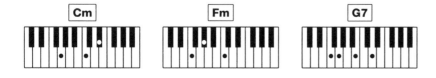

Nature Boy

Words and Music by Eden Ahbez

Suggested Registration: Acoustic Guitar
Rhythm: Rhumba
Tempo: ♩ = 100

There was a boy, ___ a ve - ry strange en -

- chant - ed boy, ___ they say he wand-ered ve - ry far, ___

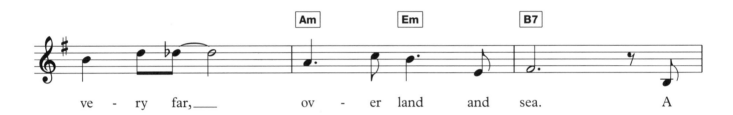

ve - ry far, ___ ov - er land and sea. A

lit - `tle shy ___ and sad of eye, ___

___ but ve - ry wise ___ was

he. And then one day, ___

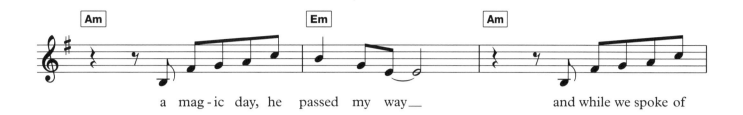

a mag-ic day, he passed my way___ and while we spoke of

ma - ny things, fools and kings,_ this he said___ to

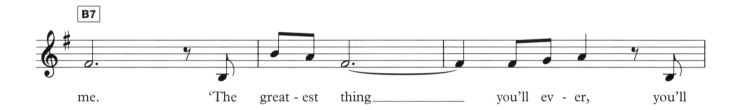

me. 'The great-est thing_____ you'll ev-er, you'll

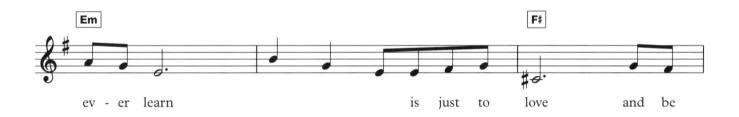

ev - er learn is just to love and be

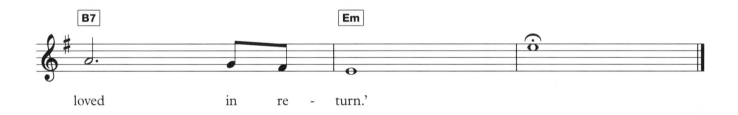

loved in re - turn.'

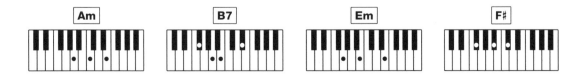

ONCE I LOVED

Words and Music by Ray Gilbert, Antonio Carlos Jobim and Vinicius De Moraes

Suggested Registration: Piano / Strings
Rhythm: Rhumba
Tempo: ♩ = 112

Oye Mi Canto

Words and Music by Gloria Estefan, Jorge Casas and Clay Ostwald

Suggested Registration: Brass
Rhythm: Salsa
Tempo: ♩ = 118

- tween, things aren't al - ways what they___ seem.
- ción en vez de de - cir a - diós.

Some - day___ it - 'll be al - right,___
Al - guien tie - ne que es - cu - char,___

chang - es___ hap - pen
O - ye es - te cion - to___ que ya

ov - er - night.___ Some - day___
va a em pe - zar. ___ Al - guien

it - 'll be al - right.___
tie - ne que es - cu - char. ___

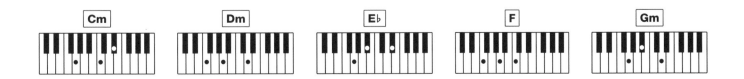

Peanut Vendor

Words by Marion Sunshine and Wolfe Gilbert
Music by Moises Simons

Suggested Registration: Solo Flute
Rhythm: Cha-Cha
Tempo: ♩ = 145

RHYTHM IS GONNA GET YOU

Words and Music by Gloria Estefan and Enrique E Garcia

Suggested Registration: Electric Piano
Rhythm: Disco
Tempo: ♩ = 120

At night__ when you turn off all the lights__ there's no

place that you can hide,___ oh, no the rhy-thm is gon-na get

_ you. In bed__ throw the cov-ers on your head,

_ you pre-tend like you were dead,___ but I know

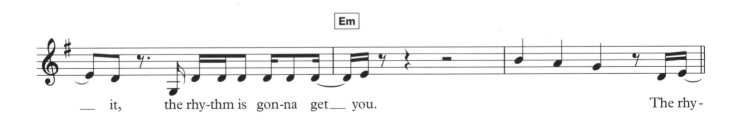

_ it, the rhy-thm is gon-na get__ you. The rhy-

-thm is gon-na get you,_ the rhy - thm is gon-na get you,_ the rhy-

C

-thm is gon-na get you,

D

the rhy - thm is gon-na get you,_____

Em

_ to - night!

The rhy-

-thm is gon-na get you,_ the rhy - thm is gon-na get you,_ the rhy-

C

-thm is gon-na get you,

D

the rhy - thm is gon-na get you,

Em

to - night!

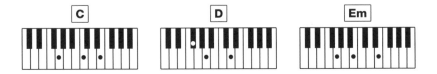

She's A Carioca

Words and Music by Ray Gilbert, Antonio Carlos Jobim and Vinicius De Moraes

Suggested Registration: Flute
Rhythm: Bossa Nova
Tempo: ♩ = 116

She's a ca - ri - oc - a, _____ she's a ca - ri - oc - a. _____

Just see the way she walk, _____ no - bo - dy else can

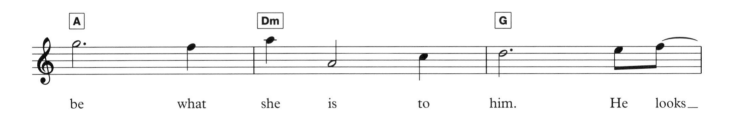

be what she is to him. He looks_____

_____ and what does he see? _____ When he looks deep _____ in her eyes,

_____ he can see the sea, a for - got - ten glow, the car -

- ess - ing skies and not on - ly that, he's in

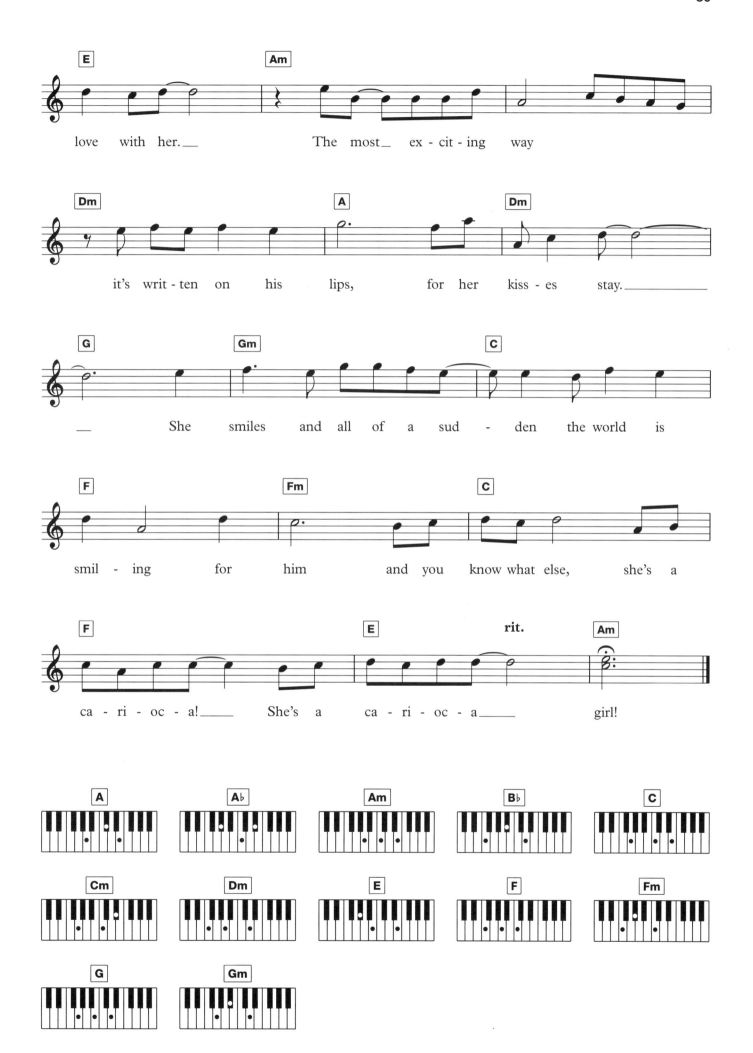

SOUL BOSSA NOVA

Words and Music by Quincy Jones

Suggested Registration: Brass
Rhythm: 8 Beat
Tempo: ♩ = 144

SWAY

Words and Music by Ruiz Beltran and Norman Gimbel

Suggested Registration: Marimba / Vibraphone
Rhythm: Rhumba
Tempo: ♩ = 120

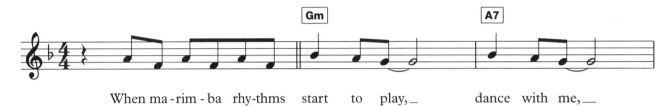

When ma-rim-ba rhy-thms start to play,__ dance with me,__

make me sway__ like the la-zy o-cean hugs the shore,

hold me close,_ sway me more__ like a flow-er bend-ing

in the breeze, bend with me,__ sway with ease.__

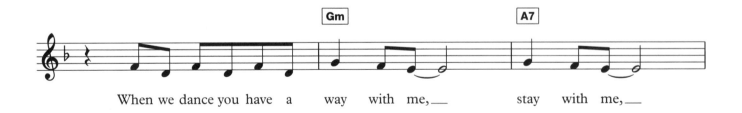

When we dance you have a way with me,__ stay with me,__

sway with me,__ oth-er danc-ers may be on the floor,

dear, but my eyes will see on - ly you. On - ly you have the

mag - ic tech-niques, when we sway, I go weak,

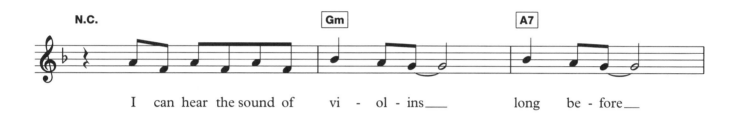

I can hear the sound of vi - ol - ins___ long be - fore___

it be - gins. ___ Make me thrill as on - ly you know how, ___

sway me smooth, sway me now. ___

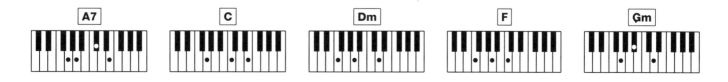

Tijuana Taxi

Words by Johnny Flamingo
Music by Bud Coleman

Suggested Registration: Trumpet
Rhythm: Swing (Shuffle)
Tempo: ♩ = 186

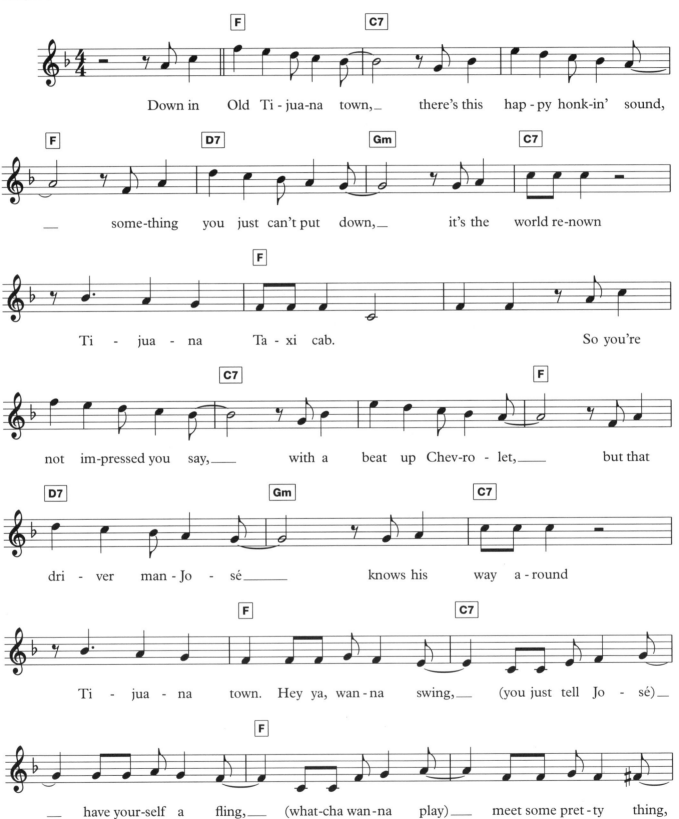

D7 **Gm**

(a - ny time you say) liv-ing like a king, _(long as you can pay)._

B♭ **B♭m** **F** **D7**

Pic - ture post-cards, 'n' hot te-qui - la, French per-fume, man, from Ve-ne-zue - la,

G7 **C7** **F**

when you're on__ a Ti-jua-na ride. So you

C7 **F**

swing and go from broke,__ not a pen - ny in your poke,__ got no

D7 **Gm** **C7**

cig - ar - ettes to smoke, but ya had your fling, the pret-ty thing and

F

ev-ery-thing is ring a ding. O - lé.

B♭ **B♭m** **C7** **D7** **F**

G7 **Gm**

Lounge Bossa

What A Diff'rence A Day Made

Words by Maria Grever
Music by Stanley Adams

Suggested Registration: Vibraphone
Rhythm: Samba
Tempo: ♩ = 120

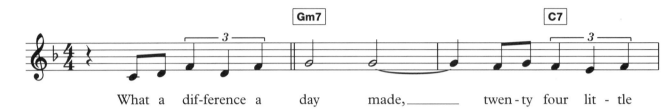

What a dif-ference a day made,_____ twen-ty four lit-tle

hou - rs_____ brought the sun and the flo - wers_____

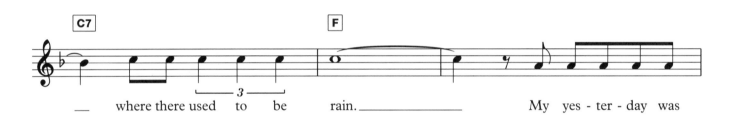

__ where there used to be rain._____ My yes-ter-day was

blue dear,_____ to-day I'm part of you dear,_____

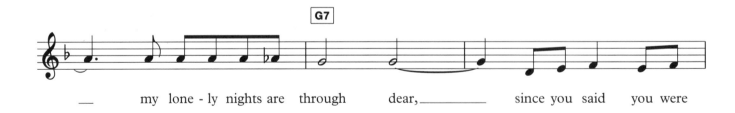

__ my lone-ly nights are through dear,_____ since you said you were

mine. What a dif-ference a day makes,_____

An expansive series of over 50 titles!

Each song features melody line, vocals, chord displays, suggested registrations and rhythm settings.

"For each title ALL the chords (both 3 finger and 4 finger) used are shown in
the correct position - which makes a change!" **Organ & Keyboard Cavalcade, May 2001**

Each song appears on two facing pages eliminating the need to turn the page during performance.
We have just introduced a new cover look to the series and will repackage the backlist in the same way.

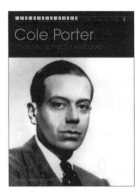